# HABITS = LIFE

# Habits = Life

BRANDY TANNER

Brandy Ellen Digital LLC

# Contents

# Chapter 1

# Dedication

This book has been a long time in the making. Throughout my life, I have constantly changed habits, lifestyle choices, relationships, and business directions.

Each time I made a change, there was either a process of trusting my instincts, something I write a lot about on Brandy-Ellen.com, or it was as simple as this cheat code system that I'm sharing with you all today and my habits = life book.

I wrote this book on Post-it notes, iPhone voice memo recordings, and computer notepad documents. All of these little pieces were compiled over the last few years to eventually put together this habit cheat code system book that will help others learn how to improve their lives.

The true inspiration behind this book is, first and foremost, my family! Without them, I probably would not be inspired or pushed to make changes to show up as a better human. Thank you for believing in me & helping around the house so I could get this writing job done; teamwork makes the dream work!

My next inspiration comes from my friends and extended family, who have always been in my corner. Thank you for not being afraid to tell me that I am stronger than I think and better than I am behaving and for knowing that I could always do better even when I made a big mistake (or two).

All of these people in my family, my extended family, and my circle of friends online and in real life are my true inspirations in this world. You all give me the strength to make it through another day, try to improve, and prove that I am worthy of your love, respect, and friendship.

As a final dedication, I would like to dedicate this book to the Lake Wentworth Inn in Wolfeboro, NH. This is the place where I finally compiled all of my voice memos, all of my note-pad documents, and all of my Post-it notes into what is now the book you are holding.

Maybe you'll get lucky and go on vacation at Lake Wentworth Inn to see a copy of this book in their library in the common area. I hope to send them a copy once published so they can place it in their common area library for the inn guests to read.

Much love,

Brandy Ellen Tanner

# Chapter 2

# Introduction

Riddle me this. Do you have a morning routine? I have asked this question over the years with different people, and I always get some people saying, "I don't have a morning routine."

*Not at all??? Wrong!!*

If you think about it, even those people who say they don't have any more morning routine still have a morning routine. They get up and do specific things every time they wake up in the morning. They may not do the same thing every day, but they probably do more of the same things than they realize. Things like taking a shower, drinking some coffee, brushing their teeth, putting makeup on, maybe putting lotion on, or eating some breakfast.

*They do whatever they do to get out of the house or to sit down and work from home.*

*This means that they have a morning routine.*

A morning routine is a set of habits you have developed over the years. These habits can come in two forms:

- Habit one is something that comes naturally, almost like autopilot. For example, this could be as simple as waking up in the morning and brushing your teeth, waking up in the morning and taking a shower, or waking up in the morning and making coffee. These are different habits you have developed over the years, and they sort of just came robotically for you.

· The next type of habit is what I will call habit number two, which I will get more into inside this book. Habit number two is things you consciously try to add to your life to feel, live, and think better. All of those things are habits that will truly help you make a fulfilling life.

So, let me go backward a little bit here. Why are habits so important to me, and why am I writing a little book about habits = life? Well, because I had this epiphany, many of the things I was doing were robotic. I kept thinking the same thoughts. I kept doing the same things. I kept craving the same things when trouble hit. I decided I no longer wanted these "things" controlling my life.

I wanted to regain control of myself. I wanted to feel more content and more peaceful. Did you know the word content used to be almost like a swear word to me? I didn't like it; it was boring, and it wasn't chaotic enough for me. This brought about much drama in my life that was unnecessary.

I know external things that happened in my life were choices, decisions, and habits from other people. I tend to start looking back at myself in hindsight 2020 and evaluating things that I want to change for me because when you do that, you open your hands and your spirit and energy to invite the right people into your circle & it flows naturally.

This is why I'm writing this book, Habits = Life. If you've been following me for some time in the 16-plus years I've been online trying to make a living (at the time of writing this book), then you probably know that I am continuously making choices that I feel are right for myself and my children.

My children are my priorities; they are my job; even after this younger one in a couple of years turns 18 at the time of writing this book, I will still have to put my kids at some level of priority. However, it will shift a little when they are adults making their own life and their habits to create their reality, but for now, I've had to learn to adjust things in my life that are good for me so that I can show up better for them thus hoping to stop making the same mistakes.

I wanted to write this book to help other people learn new ways to add new conscious habits into their lives to allow other habits to fall off and no longer be a thing.

*My mission with life = habits is that you will essentially learn my simple cheat code system to add new habits into your life, thus removing other habits that were just robotically made without much effort and stress.*

Now that I've shared a little introduction, it's time to dive deep into the stories of what brought me here to write this book. A story of different habits and journeys I've been on and how you can use those examples to learn the same technique. I call this my cheat code. I know that when you adjust your habits, you start to live, feel, breathe, and be better.

Using my habit cheat code system will allow you to succeed in your life unlike anything you've ever thought possible! Get your thinking caps on and child-like dream mind ready, for we're about to dive into the system that has helped me transform my entire life from the bottom up in the past five years. *I want you to have similar success.*

*Can't stop.*

*Won't stop.*
*Let's do this.*

# Chapter 3

# Share some Habits that You'd Like to Change

This is a space to share some of the habits you currently have that are no longer serving you. This space will help you revisit some ideas as you work through the habit cheat code system featured within the pages of this book. There are other pages similar to this throughout the book, so don't worry if you skip this part right now. You can come back to it later.

# Chapter 4

# Understanding Habits and Changing Them

Have you ever brushed your teeth without thinking about it? Or maybe you've tied your shoes so fast you didn't even notice doing it? These are examples of habits. Habits are things we do regularly, almost without thinking. They are like automatic actions or thoughts that happen without us deciding to do them.

Imagine your brain is like a supercomputer. It learns to make some actions into habits so it doesn't have to think hard about them every time. This way, your brain can save energy for more important things, like learning new math problems or deciding which game to play.

## How Do Habits Form?

Habits start by repeating something many times. Let's say every day after school, you eat a cookie. Soon, your brain starts to expect a cookie after school every day. That's how a habit forms!

A habit has three main parts::

- **Cue:** This tells your brain to start a habit. In our cookie example, the cue is coming home from school.
- **Routine:** This is the habit itself. Eating the cookie is the routine.
- **Reward:** This is what your brain likes about the habit. The yummy taste of the cookie is the reward.

When these three parts work together, they make a loop that helps the habit stick in your brain.

### Recognizing Auto-Pilot Habits

Some habits are on 'auto-pilot.' This means we do them without even noticing. For example, you might bite your nails or tap your foot without realizing it. These habits can be tricky because we don't always know we're doing them.

To find these habits, you need to become a detective. Pay attention to what you do on a regular day. Do you always watch TV after dinner? Do you snack when you're bored? These might be your auto-pilot habits.

### Why Change Habits?

Some habits are like superpowers that keep us healthy and safe. Think about brushing your teeth. Doing this twice a day keeps your teeth clean and prevents cavities. Wearing a seatbelt in the car is another excellent habit. It's like having a superhero belt that keeps you safe in case of a sudden stop or accident.

But, just like superheroes have their challenges, we sometimes face habits that aren't so helpful. For example, watching TV for many hours can be one of these habits. Watching your favorite shows is fun, but spending too much time in front of the TV means you're sitting still a lot. This can make your body feel sluggish and miss the time you could spend playing outside or reading an incredible book.

Eating too many sweets is another habit that can be tricky. Sweets taste delicious, but eating them all the time isn't the best choice for your body. Too much sugar can lead to toothaches and make you feel tired. Plus, it doesn't give you the energy to play and learn.

As you can see, we form many different habits in our lifetime, so we must pay close attention to what habits we have on autopilot and what habits could perhaps be adjusted for a better life.

This book is all about sharing my personal story of quitting smoking in 2021 using what I now call my cheat code for creating a new habit, no matter how hard it seems to get rid of the old one.

# Chapter 5

# Observing Auto-Pilot Habits

This exercise is about observing your own life. The goal is not to judge or change your habits but to become aware of them. Autopilot habits are those actions or behaviors you do without much conscious thought, often because they have become part of your routine or responses to certain environmental triggers. By identifying these, you are taking the first step towards mindfulness and, potentially, transformation.

- Identification of Auto-Pilot Habits:
  - What are the first things you do after waking up? Have you noticed any patterns?
  - Can you identify any activities you do automatically when you feel stressed, anxious, or happy?
  - Are there specific times of day when you find yourself engaging in mindless activities? What are these activities?
- Context and Triggers:
  - What external events or internal feelings trigger your auto-pilot habits?

- ○ Do certain environments or people trigger automatic behaviors more than others? Describe them.
  - ○ How do your energy levels throughout the day influence your automatic behaviors?
- · Emotions and Needs:
  - ○ How do you feel before, during, and after engaging in an auto-pilot habit?
  - ○ Do you think your auto-pilot habits are fulfilling a particular need or emotion? What might that be?
  - ○ Reflect on a recent day—were there moments you acted automatically because of how you felt? What were those moments?
- · Reflection and Awareness:
  - ○ Were there any auto-pilot habits that surprised you once you became aware of them? Why?
  - ○ How do your auto-pilot habits align with your values and goals in life?
  - ○ In what ways have your auto-pilot habits changed over time, and what influenced these changes?
- · Mindfulness and Presence:
  - ○ During a typical day, how often do you find yourself fully present in the moment versus operating on auto-pilot?
  - ○ Can you recall a moment when being on auto-pilot caused you to miss out on something important?
  - ○ What strategies can you use to become more mindful and present, especially during routine activities?

# Chapter 6

# My First BIG Habit Change Quit Smoking

It's only right that I start this book off by sharing the ultimate quit cheat code that made me come up with future habit changes and my system, my system of quitting or adding anything new into your life right so that was the day that I decided cigarettes were no longer going to be part of my life.

Quitting smoking cigarettes is essentially the number one thing that taught me there is this sort of cheat code, if you will, to change habits in your life. My first experience was about quitting smoking, and I had to create my cheat code to be successful with this habit change.

You see, I started smoking cigarettes when I was about thirteen years old, and over the years, I have quit at various times. For example, I quit for about a year, each time that would be during pregnancy, and another time I tried to quit and it just was not successful and ended up turning back to smoking cigarettes again.

This time in 2021, I knew I was ready to quit, but I revisited the times that I quit smoking and went back to it. I wanted to know what things created a temptation that called me back to smoking cigarettes even though I knew I didn't want to be a smoker.

Some of the things I realized about the temptation to smoke a cigarette after I've quit is that there are many temptations, and there'll be differences based on who you are. Just to give you a few examples of what I realized was tempting me, thus causing me to be less effective in quitting smoking:

- One thing that tempted me back to cigarettes would be drinking alcohol with people. If I were around people and drinking some beers or whatnot, I would want to have a cigarette with my alcoholic beverage, so I knew that was one major thing that always caused me to go back to smoking cigarettes for no good reason
- Another thing that tempted me to go back to smoking cigarettes Each time I quit was stressors. It's pretty funny that smoking cigarettes increases your stress response in your body in your mind, yet you want to reach for those cigarettes every time you're stressed out. Although logically, I knew this was counterproductive, it was one of the temptations that caused me to have a weakness and go back to smoking cigarettes in the past
- A third thing That caused me to go back to smoking cigarettes a lot of the time was needed that break from the chaos that ensues when you're a mostly single mom raising three kids. I noticed that spending time outside would trigger me to want to smoke. I associated a break from chaos with smoking a cigarette was a third temptation that often caused me to go back to smoking cigarettes.

As you can see these are three temptations that obviously could be retold in a new way. By this, I mean we all tell ourselves this story about ourselves. We have a personality, we have a character, so to speak, that we've created about ourselves.

*Here's an example of the story or character I had created for myself back in the day; I've been a smoker since I was 13 years old. Each time I attempted to quit, I was unsuccessful therefore, I cannot be successful in smoking cigarettes so I'm just going to keep smoking and ignore the fact that they're unhealthy for me. This is much easier to deal with as I'm raising three kids and quitting smoking doesn't seem to be as high on the priority list as I'm juggling two boys and diapers and trying to navigate the family life as a mostly single mom*

As you can see we tell ourselves these weird stories that when we share them with someone else they're like uh really really brand that's the story you're going to stick with. Back then, I always felt like my kids had to come first and I didn't get quite to the comprehension level that smoking cigarettes was reducing my lifespan thus not benefiting my children in any way, shape, or form.

Not to mention even though I went outside to smoke cigarettes, there was still some form of nicotine on my clothing and while I didn't smoke in the vehicle with them I probably occasionally smoked in my vehicle when they were in the car. This means no matter how much I thought I was being "careful" with my smoking cigarettes, I still was having some of the smoke, and lingering things went to my children without realizing it until later.

As they say, hindsight is 2020. As I say, you won't be ready to quit or create a habit until you're mentally ready. This is why I try very hard to explain that the one thing you don't want to do is be yourself up for mistakes that you've had in the past. I believe with all of my heart that we all make mistakes, and we can only change those mistakes or habits or behavioral patterns at each season in life when we are already

In 2021, I decided I was ready. I was no longer going to tell myself the dumb stray I shared above. I was no longer going to be a smoker who hides in shame because she's a smoker and doesn't want anybody to know. I was no longer going to sit and listen to people who lecture me about how hot and healthy smoking was for me.

I had finally hit my season of life where I was ready to quit smoking, and it wasn't due to any health reasons. That's the beauty of using this book for your life: You can start to adjust your life now before any chaos in the health department, both mental and physical, happens.

Although if you were reading this because you've now had a health scare, be it mental health or physical health, my heart goes out to you. I hope so much that the words in this book and my cheat code to creating better habits for a better life truly help you reverse some of the mental and physical health problems that you are facing.

# Chapter 7

# What story are you telling yourself about your habits?

# Chapter 8

# The Process for Quit Time

OK, so now we're ready to get into the nitty-gritty details of my personal cheat code system to quit smoking. This system can work for any habit in your life that you want to change. Just a quick side note I have used this simple cheat code system to eat healthier, lose weight, live happier, and so many other things

I am beyond thrilled to share the process of quitting smoking as my simple cheat code system to help you get inspired to make these changes in your life as well. Okay, enough of my passion speaking about how things can change your life. This cheat code is so awesome it's just I'm excited to figure out a simple process that will resonate with so many of you out there.

So the process for quitting time, at least as it pertained to quitting smoking, and my friends this is exactly where the magic starts to happen. Now I will share with you the simple steps, but please remember simple does not equal easy. Well, I believe the steps are simple and pretty straightforward, sometimes also common sense steps They are not always easy to implement in your life.

I've said it before, and I say it again if you are not ready to make a change in your life, then these steps will seem very overwhelming, they will seem very difficult, and you will just freeze. Please read through these simple steps that I used to not only quit smoking but then implement them in other areas of my life read them more than once if you need to, and if you have any questions, you always can reach out to me personally on social media have no fear I'm here to help you through the process in any way I can.

## What are the simple steps to changing your life today?

Here we go, so the simple steps to changing your life today are the exact steps I took to quit smoking. What I want you to do is choose one thing that you'd like to change and then ask yourself the following questions:

- What habits in my life do I associate with this habit that I'd like to change?
- Is there anyone in my life who could perhaps be a buddy for me to be held accountable during the process of changing this habit?
- Who are the people in my life who may unintentionally make it difficult to change this habit in my life?
- What environment will help me be more successful with the mission to change my habits?
- What do I need to remove from my life before I'm ready to dive into the first step of changing this habit?
  Now you don't have to ask yourself all of those questions, but those are just a few examples of the things to think about when you're ready to make a big change.
  For me, I knew I needed to figure out what I associated

smoking cigarettes with, What story was I telling my-self about smoking cigarettes that I had to change, And lastly, what things in my life I associated with smoking a cigarette.

I realized after asking myself very similar questions to the bullet point list above that I did indeed have some-one in my life who could quit smoking with me, which is a total bonus if you can find someone like that. I also realized that drinking any sort of alcohol would be a temptation during the process of quitting smoking.

Lastly, I knew that in the past, quitting smoking nicotine patches had helped me a little bit, so I thought I would make sure I grab supplies to help me be very successful with changing this habit.

For my quitting smoking mission, I was sure to buy some okay smokes, which were CBD cigarettes, and some nico-tine patches just to make sure that I had some tools on hand in case they were a necessary backup to ease out of that nicotine habit. I'll be honest with you. I didn't like the CBD smokes because I felt like they were going to Be very similar to trading one habit for a different habit. Smoking CBD cigs is the same as smoking a cig so I didn't want to do that but I was grateful that I had them on hand to try before my brain went aha, you don't want to trade one for the other.

The nicotine patches were also not used during this pro-cess because I remembered that I actually had an adverse reaction to them years ago and I also knew that it was just this mental thing psychological thing like if I had them on anyway couldn't smoke a cigarette I'd have a stroke. And since in 2019 I had blood pressure high enough to have a stroke, I didn't want to play around with that in 2021.

So there you have it; there are some things that you need

to ask yourself kind of to review beforehand and get to know what the things you need to have in place to be successful because, let's face it, there's no other choice but to be successful with this habit change.

*You already know you are capable and will be successful this time.*

## Work Through the Questions

· What habits in my life do I associate with this habit that I'd like to change?
· Is there anyone in my life who could perhaps be a buddy for me to be held accountable during the process of changing this habit?
· Who are the people in my life who may unintentionally make it difficult to change this habit in my life?
· What environment will help me be more successful with the mission to change my habits?
· What do I need to remove from my life before I'm ready to dive into the first step of changing this habit?

# Chapter 9

# Journal Pages

# Chapter 10

# How does this habit make you feel?

Okay friends, so now we're nearing the middle part of the changing a habit process and using my cheat code system to quit or add a big habit into your life. This next step is all about how this habit makes you feel right.

Just to continue using my personal case study of quitting smoking in 2021, here is how I thought about how this habit makes me feel so that I felt a little more inspired to quit as well as no more about why am I even doing this in the first place.

As it pertains to smoking cigarettes, I had to think about what my behavior was like, so I mentioned I believe a few people knew I smoked cigarettes I even remember going to a blogging conference and not wanting to smoke cigarettes or wanting to go hide somewhere for a cigarette because I was embarrassed or shameful or whatever it was because I knew a lot of people didn't really approve of smoking cigarettes and I even honestly had a therapist one time tell me I can't be a positive lifestyle writer if I'm smoking cigarettes.

So having all of these people around me throughout my life telling me that smoking was bad led me to feel kind of shameful about them and embarrassed, so I would often hide this habit from other people.

One of the biggest things that I've learned on my self-reflection journey here in my 40s is that if I'm doing something that makes me feel embarrassed, shameful, or any sort of awkward feeling like that, then maybe it's not something I should be doing or maybe it's something I should be more confident in doing.

How do you know which is which? How do you know if this is a habit you should stop doing because you feel shameful and embarrassed or a habit that you should just be more confident in your life right?

Because let's face it, I've been doing whole 30 for 30 days at the time of writing this book. It's kind of awkward and weird to talk to other people about how excited I am to have my, you know, whole 30 foods and veggies and proteins and healthy fats II feel this way because I know the healthy fats topic is going to cause people to share their overly strong opinions about food and healthy fats.

I know that there are studies to back up what you think about food out there on the Internet. However, I still feel the way I feel about food, so I know the whole 30 challenge, some could say, is not a bad habit I am eating healthier and have more energy, but I'm feeling a little nervous to share my opinions on it for fear of backlash about it.

The embarrassment of smoking cigarettes and wanting to hide that habit made me feel dirty, less than worthy, not of a certain class level, and not as successful as some of the other people who didn't smoke cigarettes. Those sorts of things make this habit a bad habit one which should not be part of my life because I'm feeling embarrassed and I'm feeling dirty ish about smoking a cigarette.

On the other hand, the topic example of my whole 30 discussions around food and eating healthier and not wanting to share a lot about it in a passionate way is more from a fear of backlash about it. If you have a habit that you can sit down and figure out is a healthy habit, but it makes you feel sort of fearful to share it, that doesn't mean it's something that needs to go it means you need to work on something completely different within yourself which I will get into in another course and another book.

For the sake of this particular book, I'd like to focus on my quitting story as it's all about sharing that I felt ashamed, I felt dirty I felt less unworthy I did not feel confident smoking cigarettes around people which meant it was a habit that had to go.

# Chapter 11

# Journal Through These Feelings about your Habit

# Chapter 12

# More on Feelings and Habits

Good habits usually make you feel awesome! They're like your daily helpers, making each day a bit better. Think about how clean your mouth feels after brushing your teeth. That's a good habit, making you feel good, right? Or when you study a bit every day and feel super proud during a test – that's another fantastic habit!

But not every habit is good for you. Sometimes, we have habits that don't leave us feeling too great. Maybe you overeat candy and end up with a tummy ache. Or perhaps you spend loads of time playing video games and then feel bummed because you didn't get to play outside. These feelings are like little signals, telling you a habit might not be the best for you.

Your feelings are like messengers. They tell you if something is good or not for you. When a habit makes you feel happy, strong, or proud, it's probably a keeper. But if a habit often leaves you sad, tired, or sick, it might be time to rethink it.

Here are a few ways to check your habits and learn more about what you want to change or not change in your life:

- **Start a Habit Diary:** Jot down your habits and how they make you feel. Keep track for a week. Do you read before bed? How does that make you feel? Write it all down!
- **Talk About Your Habits:** Why not share your habit diary with someone you trust, like your parents or a teacher? They can help you think more about your habits and feelings.
- **Dream Big and Match Your Habits:** What are your dreams? Maybe you want to ace soccer or become an amazing artist. Do your habits help you reach these goals? If they do, they're probably good habits.

Found a habit that doesn't make you feel good? No worries! You've got this. Let's say you watch too much TV and it makes you feel lazy. Why not change that habit by watching just one show daily and then heading outside for fun?

Creating new habits that make you feel fantastic is super exciting! Want to feel healthier? How about starting a habit of walking your dog every day? Want to boost your brainpower? Try reading for 20 minutes before bed.

Your habits are a big part of who you are. They can make you feel good or not so good. By paying attention to how your habits make you feel, you can choose which ones to keep and which to switch up. This way, you ensure your habits help you be your absolute best version of yourself!

# Chapter 13

# What are your temptations?

Alright, guys let's get into the topic of what are your temptations. I'm going to just share my example again because I feel sharing my example through my story helps give a more personal experience of what your temptations are and how to handle them as you're going through this process of redefining who you are and changing the habits in your life.

For me, I knew the biggest temptation was alcohol. I knew to be successful this time around with quitting smoking cigarettes that, I was going to have to get rid of alcohol for a bit of time before I made the transition to removing cigarettes from my life.

So, how was I going to get rid of this first temptation before moving on to my mission to quit smoking for good?

This is how I did the process:

- I thought about how long I should remove alcohol from my life before being able to transition to the next step, which would be to cut cigarettes out of my life.

- This would allow me to set a quit date for my smoking, AKA my quit smoking quit date.
- Thus providing me with some sort of end date for when I needed to switch from my focus of quitting drinking to quitting smoking.

Now, I'm going to be honest with you. I don't remember if I quit alcohol for one month or three months before I quit smoking, but somewhere between one to 3 months, I decided to stop drinking any alcohol. Which led to me drinking all of the alcohol in the house before quit drinking day came; I do not recommend that step just get rid of the alcohol if that is one of the steps in your thing, just put it out like give it away to people that are old enough to drink and can drink it.

I think that if you binge drink alcohol, for most people, especially if it's an addiction, then binge drinking all the alcohol in their house over some time before you have to quit doing it might make it very difficult to stop drinking in the first place, which is why I don't recommend that step for people who are trying to quit drinking and it is a problem for them.

So, during the one to three months of not drinking alcohol, I prepared myself by buying the supplies I noted above earlier on in this book right so that I would be ready to transition from quitting alcohol to quitting smoking. I found that quitting alcohol was not that hard. I'm sure I had some days where I was like, "Man, this is hard". I was so used to having a couple of drinks at the end of the day to ease my mind, but it wasn't that bad overall.

Side Note: The reason quitting alcohol wasn't as bad for me as the idea of no longer smoking forever is because alcohol did not have control over me. While I do turn to alcohol for various reasons, I've learned over the years I actually can control my response and not reach for that drink whereas cigarettes were controlling my life and I couldn't seem to stop smoking them.

For this particular habit of smoking cigarettes, my biggest temptation was the alcohol part. For your habit that you're looking to change you may have more than one temptation if that is the case then you should check the temptations off one at a time.

# Chapter 14

# Finding Hidden Temptations

Changing habits is like going on a treasure hunt. You're the brave explorer, and treasure is your new, better habit. But, just like in any adventure, there are challenges. These challenges are often temptations that make it hard to stick to your new habit. Let's learn how to spot these hidden temptations.

Temptations are tricky because they're things we like, but they might not be good for our new habit. Imagine you're trying to eat less candy. But then, you see a big bowl of your favorite sweets on the kitchen table. That's a temptation! It's sitting there, looking yummy and making it hard to remember your new habit of eating healthy snacks.

To find your temptations, consider what you love that might stop you from your new habit. Do video games make it hard to find time for homework? Does staying up late make it challenging to wake up early? These are your temptations.

Remember, it's okay to like these things. The trick is to balance them with your new habit. Maybe play video games only after homework or choose one night a week for a late bedtime. By understanding your temptations, you can plan how to handle them without giving up on your new habit.

Changing habits is a journey with ups and downs. Finding and understanding your temptations is a big step in winning this exciting adventure!

# Chapter 15

# Write Down Temptations that May Deter you from Succeeding With this Habit Change

# Chapter 16

# How to Handle Multiple Temptations

To answer your question on how to handle temptations that need to go before a significant habit change when you have more than one temptation that you foresee getting in the way of having success with this habit change would tell you to take it one step at a time.

For me, I know that I'd have to go at least one month without whatever temptation it was that I need to get rid of so for example, if you have three temptations that you need to get rid of to step forward for this significant habit change then you should take three months minimum to change each of those three habits one by one so at the end of the 3-month term you can focus on the new big habit that you're looking to add or remove from your life.

The schedule for removing three temptations from your life before the BIG remove or add habit day for the thing you're trying to change may look something like this:

- Month 1 leading up to the significant habit change is going to be choosing one of the easier things to remove as a temptation. Set a stop date for that, and make sure it's about three months before the "official begin or quit date for the BIG habit change."
- Month 2 leading up to the significant habit change is going to be choosing the next not-so-easy temptation to remove from your life for maximum success with the "official begin or quit date for the BIG habit change."
- Month 3 leading up to the significant habit change is going to be choosing the third and probably the hardest temptation to remove from your life for ultimate success with the "official begin or quiet date for the BIG habit change.'

The above bullet points give you an example of how to remove three temptations from your life before you focus on that big change you're looking to make. As you can tell from my personal story of quitting smoking for good in 2021, I only had one major challenge or temptation, and that was alcohol.

With that being said, other people may have more temptations than just alcohol when it comes to quitting smoking, and I'm honestly sure I probably had other temptations. Still, they weren't things that I needed to focus an entire month on removing.

The best way for you to succeed with changing this habit is to really be honest with yourself and maybe ask some of your close relatives or friends what they think you need to do as a baby step before you jump into this big habit change.

No matter what this new habit change is, you'll feel better when you receive feedback from friends and family who may be able to give more insight on what temptations and baby steps should occur before the BIG habit change day.

I've learned something in my 40s: sometimes I'm a little tunnel-visioned or rose-colored glasses about the things I think I need to remove or add to my life. This is where I've started to ask trusted people and/or people living in a way that I want to live for specific advice on how to succeed with whatever I'm trying to do in my life.

This is why I always suggest to my life coaching clients to ask people that they trust about some of the habits that they should adjust in their life for maximum success with whatever goals they have in their world. Your trusted circle may give you productive feedback to implement this habit change so that it sticks.

If you can be open-minded and open-hearted enough to ask the right people for the right tips and advice during this process, you'll honestly have a higher chance of success in quitting a habit or adding a new habit into your life.

If you're struggling with temptations, I truly want you to ask these close people in your life who know you well, for the temptations list because, honestly, it's sometimes hard to look yourself in the mirror and be like, man, "That is a temptation".

It's a hard pill to swallow at first. Just be sure to give yourself some grace, talk to your friends and family with an open mind, and learn more about the different things that tempt you from what you truly want.

# Chapter 17

# Brainstorm Your Temptations that Need to Change for Success with This Habit Change

# Chapter 18

# My Process of Evaluating the Feelings with Habits

I think the biggest way to learn about which habit needs to stay or which habit needs to go is to think about my example laid out above about the whole 30 diet conversation versus the smoking conversation.

I believe that if habit needs to go away and be replaced with something healthier if it causes you stress anxiety animosity depression any sort of what I call non-normal human emotions and feelings. Suppose you think about this thing like in my story of smoking cigarettes and your stomach is in a knot and it's not something that you feel comfortable having in your life. In that case, your entire body and nervous system are saying you need to get rid of this habit for something better.

*I keep using the word "simple," but I want you to know simple does not equate to "easy".*

The step of learning about which habits need to stay or which habits need to go is all about picking a habit that makes you feel non-normal human emotions, meaning it doesn't make you feel joy, it doesn't make you feel confident, it doesn't make you feel content.

This habit makes you feel embarrassed, shameful, or dirty. Those are reasons to kind of figure out how you can adjust this habit that you're looking to change to live a better life.

Sometimes I use a pros and cons list with different habits to see if there are more pros than cons with this habit. If there are more cons than pros, then I look at this habit or the different habits that I'm evaluating, and I start with a simple habit.

*That's how I feel you will have the most success; start with a smaller habit to change.*

As you can imagine, quitting smoking was probably one of the harder habits that I've done over the past three years or four years, but it isn't the only habit that I've changed. Since quitting smoking was one of the hardest things I've done in the last three or four years, I decided to use it as my case example.

I wanted to show how this simple concept and process can change even the hardest habits in your life. That said, if you're new to this and trying to look inward and change your life for the better, I invite you to look at a tiny habit evaluate how it makes you feel, and do a pros and cons list.

Start with a smaller habit that you need to change first because sometimes people just need to start with something easy to get the gist of doing this habit-changing exercise.

There is absolutely no right or wrong way to do this. At the end of the day, my wish for you is to use my story and use these examples inside this book as a way to morph it into something that works for you so that every day you wake up you're inspired to be better than you were yesterday.

I want you to be inspired to continue changing one habit at a time. That way, you can stand tall and proud when you look back a year, two years, or more from now to see just how awesome you've become over the years. I want you to begin to feel that confidence increase as you use my cheat code system to change one habit at a time over your entire lifespan. I want you to feel confident that you're using this system to take charge of your mental and physical health to improve yourself.

# Chapter 19

# Pros & Cons List

# Chapter 20

# The Simple Cheat Code Process Summarized

Now that you have gone through the whole process of what a habit is and why you should change your habits, the temptations that may make it difficult to change this habit and how these different habits make you feel along with some of the information and how I utilized these tips of this cheat code system to quit smoking in 2021 it's time for me to summarize this cheat code process to help you with a more fluid approach to utilizing the bigger picture of all that I shared in a simple step by step way.

*The Steps in Order:*

- · What habits do you have, how do they make you feel, and which ones are easier to start with for this change?
- · What are the temptations for you regarding this habit you're focused on changing?

- What do your friends, family, and others say are your real temptations for this habit that you've grown accustomed to?
- How long do you need to work on the temptations before moving into the big step of changing your BIG habit?
- Schedule a start date for removing the BIG habit based on how long you need to work on the temptations (I advise 30 days per temptation).
- Start the process ... remove temptation for 30 days, but don't forget to get a support system!

The key to success is to find a support group online, in real life, or just reach out to friends and family to see if you can get them for support whenever you're feeling tempted. They should be people who you know will not allow you to be led into temptation. This process may not work the first time or even the second time; remember it took me over three times before I finally quit smoking for good in 2021.

It's OK to fall back and get yourself back into the process of my steps for creating a beautiful life through changing one simple habit at a time. Come back and repeat this process every few months to ensure you're constantly working on showing up as a better YOU with each passing "season in life."

# Chapter 21

# Work Through The Steps

# Chapter 22

# Revisit this Process Every Few Months to Make New Habits

In the previous pages, I said that I revisited this process every few months, and the reason is that we are human beings who get accustomed to living in this autopilot mode. It happens to the best of us for good and for not-so-good reasons. I think that as humans, we just tend to feel more comfortable in our lives, and we just let it flow until one day we wake up and we're like, why do we feel empty?

I don't know about you, but I'm going to say that because you bought this book, you also want to be proactive and feel like you have some control over something in your life. That means every so often, you may want to revisit this book and the simple cheat code system for changing a habit and maybe buy a habit tracker workbook.

I have habit tracker workbooks sold separately so that you can work through some more changes that you will need to make three to 6 months from now.

I hope this book provides you with a way to be proactive and not beat yourself up about new habits that formed or living on autopilot again without meaning to or anything like that because, remember, you are human.

*Every single one of us human beings just gets accustomed to living life a certain way and it's neither good nor bad it's just how it is.*

That's why you really need to revisit this process every few months to make new habits and if not, to make new habits, just to revisit your life and see if you are getting in the right mindset every day.

*Do you wake up joyous or content with your life?*

*Do you feel like things are going in the right direction for you, or have you started to feel like things are spiraling down, or you've lost momentum or creativity?*

Those are some questions to ask yourself every few months. These pauses to ask such questions are the best way to do some inner work so that you never let yourself get on autopilot again. Try to have a journal, or you can use my habit tracking workbook because those are the best ways to track yourself and figure out where you're at in life, what's going on in your head, and what's going on in your world that maybe you need to revisit and change.

I'll give you one last secret in this book as to what I use as my telltale sign that things aren't going so well: The best way for me to tell when things are not going the right way or maybe I've just gotten on autopilot is to recognize how I'm feeling internally.

I also analyze how I'm responding to someone in my close circle of friends, see their facial expressions, and read their body language. If someone close to me seems to be sad or like pushed down or just feeling bad about something I said, I can see it in their face, and I realize that I'm not being my best self.

This is the moment when I take the time to use my habit tracking workbook and my journal notebooks to figure out what is going on with me. Sometimes it means I have to take a little solo vacation to work on myself so that I can come back and be the amazing person and loving person that I'm meant to be.

I believe that you and I are supposed to be loving, kind-hearted people. We are all here having a human experience and have ups and downs. There are challenges in each of our lives. While each challenge or scenario in each other's lives may look different, the ultimate feelings are the same: you start to feel glum, sad, withdrawn, and not valuable. Your self-doubt creeps in and takes control of your life, and all of those things compile up to the point of you want to explode or you want to sleep for days.

Having this book Habits = Life as your guidebook to realize that you are not alone, that you can make a change, and that people like you are out there trying to survive can help you transform your life for something far better than you can imagine.

# Chapter 23

# Journal Your Way To Success with this Habit Change

What habit do you want to change, and why?

How can you adjust your environment to support your new habit?

· How will you monitor your progress?
· What will you do if you experience a setback?
· How will you celebrate your successes?
· How can you incorporate this new habit into your identity, so
it becomes a part of who you are?

What have you learned about yourself through this process?

How has your life improved as a result of this change?

What adjustments, if any, do you need to make to your approach to continue making progress?

How can you apply what you've learned from this experience to other areas of your life?

# Chapter 24

# Final Thoughts from Brandy

First off I want to thank you for taking the time to read my book; it means the world to me that you were able to buy this book and at least read it! Whether you implement my strategies or you don't implement my strategies right now, I know that this book has sparked some sort of life back into you.

I am confident that if you read this and allow yourself some time to process all that is inside of it you will soon find that you are inspired to take a little tiny action in your life for the better. I know that changing habits and becoming a new person is extremely hard.

Some things that will happen as you change your habits are that your friend group may change, your income may change, and your lifestyle may change, but one thing is for sure: *it will be for the better!*

I'd like to finish this book with a thank you for reading this book and taking the time to show interest in yourself. The second tidbit of information I'd like to share with you is to remember that during this process it will be difficult and people around you will maybe think you're crazy and you may no longer fit in with the same friend group.

Not fitting in with the same friends group or even fitting in with your family members that you previously fit in with is the hardest part of changing your autopilot habits in life. I want you to know that as you feel inspired to keep changing yourself for the better, you'll also feel the mourning process of losing friends and family members on some level.

I want you to know that if you keep trying to change these habits for the better and you use my cheat code system, the right people and your new tribe will eventually find you.

*Be sure to track your progress online through your private Facebook profile, a private journal app, a public Instagram channel, or even over on Twitter, which is now known as X.*

When you start to share your everyday habits and the changes you'll notice that new people find you! You'll have some followers or friends or connections fall off; they may un-follow you on social media, but you'll have so many more new people who will join you and be inspired by the little habits and changes that you're making in your life that you won't be mourning the loss of the older connections as much.

I truly hope this book has inspired you to make small changes in your life toward a better lifestyle. As a means to help you with your continued efforts to live better and be a better person, I wanted to open my arms and my social media out to you guys below, you will find the links to my social media accounts that I'm mostly active on.

I invite you to go ahead and like and/or follow me on the two social media accounts below so that you can follow along on my journey as I continue to change new habits in my life and continue to learn and grow.

*I would love for you to be in my circle of friends on the Internet.*

Not only that, but my inbox is open to anyone who has bought this book and has some more questions. Perhaps you feel like I could elaborate on some of the steps a little bit more or just need some clarification or guidance.

I would love to help you on your journey to make new habits for a better life, so do not hesitate to reach out to me. Just remember that my inbox fills up pretty quickly these days, so I may take some time to respond and I may not be able to respond to every single message, but I will do my best to respond and assist.

Thank you again for your time and your support. I appreciate you, and I'm sending love and light your way toward success in all of your future endeavors in life, business, and love.

**Instagram:** Instagram.com/brandyellen1
**Facebook:** Facebook.com/brandyellen
**Website:** CoachBrandy.com